D1247580

HEROD AND MARIAMNE

Herod and Mariamne

PÄR LAGERKVIST

Translated from the Swedish by Naomi Walford

1969   New York   Alfred·A·Knopf

This is a Borzoi Book
Published by Alfred A. Knopf, Inc.

Published October 10, 1968
Second Printing, February 1969
First American Edition
Copyright © 1968 by Chatto & Windus Ltd.
All rights reserved under International
and Pan-American Copyright Conventions.
Published in the United States
by Alfred A. Knopf, Inc., New York,
and in Great Britain as MARIAMNE
by Chatto & Windus Ltd., London.
Originally published in Sweden
as MARIAMNE *by Albert Bonnier Stockholm.*
© 1967 by Pär Lagerkvist.
Distributed by Random House, Inc., New York.
Library of Congress Catalog Card Number: 68–23949
Manufactured in the United States of America

HEROD AND MARIAMNE

hen Herod the great king lived his life here on earth he was a mighty man, whose like perhaps has never been known. Or so he himself believed—and he may have been right. He was an emblem of mankind: mankind that replenishes the earth but whose race shall one day be erased from it and, so far as may be conjectured, will leave no memorial. But let us now turn from this, and tell his story.

He was king of the Jews, but his people did not love him; partly because of his great wickedness and partly because he was an Edomite, and therefore imperfectly circumcised in that only a portion of the foreskin had been removed, as was the Edomite custom. His many evil deeds caused them to hate him more and more the longer he lived, and to desire his death. Nevertheless, for all his wickedness

7

he built a temple to the Lord which surpassed even Solomon's in glory. The Jews were much astonished, but although they could not deny the beauty of the temple, their hatred of him in no way diminished. They regarded him as the cruellest, most ungodly man who had ever lived—as the scum of the human race—and he filled them with loathing, disgust, and fear. Such was their judgment, and none can deny that it was just and true.

And he loved Mariamne.

Although he was a native of Jerusalem, his true homeland was the desert, the land of his forefathers, which had given them their soul. All unawares he bore the desert within him, and at times he felt its vast desolation. But he possessed also his people's wild joy in life—joy in violence, blood, and battle; joy in rampant horses trampling bleed-

8

ing enemies underfoot; joy in killing and in the
resulting lust for living; joy in fugitives and the
wounded, in the capture and rape of women, and
in all that war brings with it when auspicious and
ably conducted; joy in success, gold, power—in a
word, joy in life entire. Reverses—for he had those
too—filled him with like exhilaration, for his hatred of those who inflicted defeat upon him was
savage, inflaming him to a fury which, contained
and well-concealed from others, bided its time for
revenge and renewed conflict. But ill fortune in
such matters as women filled him rather with an
inner desolation which was surely part of the void
and loneliness in his desert soul.

He was a big man, somewhat heavily built, with
coarse features; not handsome, perhaps, but once
seen not soon forgotten. At least, the look in his

9

eyes was not forgotten, although it was encountered unwillingly and for no longer than necessary. That gaze was dangerously observant; with it he formed his judgments of men; and clearly he disliked them. His eyes were brown with lighter flecks in them: some called them lion eyes, but they were wrong. The eyes of a lion are much paler. His complexion was yellowish, as were his lips; no wholesome colour, although in other ways he seemed full of vitality and health. Some believed him to be sick and near to death, but in this they were mistaken: he did not die.

Although not exactly lame, he trod more heavily on his right foot than on his left. He himself was probably unaware of this, but others noticed it and thought it lent more force and somehow more menace to his figure, especially when seen from behind as he broke off a conversation and walked away. But this may have been because at such times he was often angered, and his wordless departure boded ill.

Almost all encounters with him seemed ominous. It was best to avoid the necessity of appearing before him, or any meeting.

A bloody road had led him to the throne, the throne of David and Solomon; and his first act after his accession was one of revenge upon those who had sought to prevent him from seizing it. He never forgot being brought before the Great Council, the Sanhedrin, because of his deeds of violence; nor did he forget those who had helped to bring him there. They did not long survive, although they were venerated elders of the highest priesthood in Israel. He despised priests; he mocked both them and the god they clung to and worshipped in their dilapidated old temple, which they revered for its antiquity and in which nothing might be altered either in the building itself or in the Lord's service. Others too, who had either opposed him in the past or might be thought to do so in the future, fell victim to the massacre he instituted immediately upon his accession to power.

Two years later, with the help of the Romans, he laid siege to Jerusalem, his own rebellious capital, and after its fall he allowed those polluted heathens to loot and murder until the streets were strewn with corpses and the very sanctuary was filled with dead and dying. Small wonder that his people hated him and regarded him as a monster in human form.

How was it, then, that not many years later this same man conceived the idea of building a temple to the god in whom he did not believe? A glorious temple, a temple without peer.

How was it possible? How can it be explained?

12

It was believed by all who watched the temple rise—and is believed to this day by those who reflect at all upon the story of Herod's life—that he was impelled by arrogance and vanity to outshine Solomon himself, upon whose throne it was alleged he had no right to sit—yes, even to surpass the celebrated temples of Rome; that it was to glorify himself that he did it, so that his name might be handed down to posterity and he himself become immortal.

And surely this was true. His greed for glory was insatiable: it knew no bounds. It was his motive for building the temple: if anyone had questioned him he would have acknowledged this, and been surprised that such a query was deemed necessary.

He followed the progress of the construction with lively interest, watching everything, supervising everything meticulously; and he would often

13

stand plunged in contemplation of his work—of himself.

Often too, when unable to sleep, he left his palace in the middle of the night and went to his temple. At such an hour it was deserted, and he was quite alone on his wanderings. Alone in his temple.

He walked there in the darkness, with his heavy tread.

On leaving it to return to the palace, he would often linger for a while looking up at the starry sky and let the stars plunge their spears into his lonely desert soul, of which he knew nothing.

For he was a man of action, oriented outward, on outward events. He never thought about himself: he was what he was.

It was with deep mistrust that the Jews watched the construction of a temple by so sinful a man, one

guilty of so many bloody deeds; a man not really
of the tribe of Judah, and imperfectly circumcised.
They were outraged that he should be building a
house to the Lord. How could the Lord allow it?

Certainly it promised to be a fair, rich temple,
with walls of marble—a foreign stone brought from
afar, from another country—and adorned with gold
and silver, with copper and with Corinthian bronze,
the most costly material of all. But did the Lord
desire such a dwelling place? Did He really? Was
not all this alien magnificence an abomination to
Him?

If the temple had of necessity to be rebuilt, would
He not rather that all the stone should be hewn
from the rock about His own city, from His own
hills? Would He not?

The Lord's will was hard to interpret, yet insofar
as one could know anything of Him one must believe that this was what He would wish.

15

Surely He did not desire such magnificence both within and without, such richness and adornment, but would prefer something more like the old temple—more like Himself.

One could not be sure. One could never be quite sure what the Lord's will was. But the high priest, who stood nearest of all to Him, was of the opinion that however rich and fair this new building promised to be, the Lord, like His servants, would have preferred everything to remain as it had been in the old days.

Yet the Lord did not cause the walls to collapse, as He could well have done if He had utterly abhorred this temple raised by an evildoer. This may have been because the old temple was not pulled down all at once, but was replaced bit by bit with new walls; and because within it the service of the Lord continued uninterrupted (though of course not undisturbed) by the building process, and

16

without the break in worship which had been dreaded above all by priesthood and people. For nothing was so needful as to serve the Lord daily.

One must admit that Herod himself ordained that the work should be done in this way, with a consideration remarkable in a criminal, a desecrator of all things holy.

Yet it must also be said that this in no way altered his people's opinion of him, nor had they any reason to change their minds. He remained what he had always been, and his evil deeds both in Jerusalem and in the surrounding countryside spread terror in the path of his mercenaries. Most of these men were of foreign origin and without pity for the chosen people of the Lord. It was by the help of these hirelings that Herod was able to maintain his sovereignty and his throne. They liked him because he allowed them to do as they pleased: to plunder and massacre his enemies, and those sus-

17

pected of being his enemies, and to confiscate their property both on their own and on their ruler's behalf. They resembled their master and were therefore devoted to him.

These things were known to everyone, and a mist of blood seemed to hang about Herod, about his massive figure—seldom seen but always sensed—whether in his palace or in some unknown corner of his kingdom where evil was intended.

Few came to his palace, and little was known of what went on within it. Life there was said to be dissolute, among heathen women of unknown race and vile, unknown vices, and he himself was said to be the most vicious of all.

No wonder, it was whispered—his spies were everywhere—no wonder! For his race originated in that land of all vices, the land of Sodom and Gomorrah, which the Lord had since made a wilderness.

But little was really known of this. The truth was that he was cruel and violent in his dealings with women, without consideration for anyone but himself. His contempt for them was frank and brutal, and he carried his innate violence into his relations with them. Like any Oriental prince he always had women about him, and his courtiers kept him supplied with fresh ones, to curry favour with him, and took them over when he tired of them. As a rule he tired of them quite soon. Once they had satisfied him they merely bored him. Yet now and then he did keep the same one by him for a while, which surprised those nearest to him and brought about a temporary change in the palace. But he loved no one, and no one loved him.

A vicious life, no doubt; yet perhaps not exactly for the reasons given by the people. It may have been sinful because it was so joyless; for an empty, joyless life it must be where love itself is evil.

19

Though indeed cruelty may bring with it a kind of joy.

So both the building and life in the palace continued; the life was regarded as sinful, and was so, albeit for other reasons. Also he continued his solitary nocturnal walks in the temple, his own temple, and under the starry sky above the Holy Land, whose king he was.

But for long periods he was absent from his capital, on wild rides at the head of his men, to fight, to strike down his adversaries or fancied adversaries—any who might intend to rob him of his power and seize it for themselves. It was a life on horseback and it suited him entirely, better than any other kind. It was the life of his forebears, such as they

20

had led in their desert realms to the south, with raids into Judea and attacks on the caravans bound thither. It was a hard, cruel life, and he felt in him his fathers' wild blood and their wild joy in living— in living life as it really was, the life of his ancestors, the life that had given him his soul.

But the Jews said:

"He is a desert man. That is why we have to endure it."

nd he met Mariamne.

A He was standing on the road to Damascus, only a little way beyond the gate of the city, as she came by. It was as simple as that, and yet the moment when it happened was so different from the moment before that nothing could ever be the same again: neither the sunlight, nor the ground, nor the cropped grass on the ground, nor the flowers in that short grass. Sheep had nibbled the grass but left the flowers untouched. What flowers were they? He had never seen them before. They had been there always, but he would not have noticed them if she had not passed by.

He saw her only briefly, but that moment was like no other moment in his life—like nothing he had ever experienced. He did not understand it at all; he knew only that something strange and impossible to explain had happened. Then she was gone. She was there no longer.

He laid his hand over his eyes so as not to forget what he had seen, and so as to see nothing else.

He had never done such a thing before. It felt odd to stand there with his hand over his eyes; people might wonder at it. They might think he was shading his eyes from the sun. But he was not.

We must tell of what he had seen; what reality it was that lay behind the experience, and moved him thus.

She who passed by was young and seemed fragile, and unusually fair for a Jewish woman. She was dressed, like the more distinguished ladies, in the Greek manner, and had laid a corner of her white linen mantle over her head, over her fair hair. Strangely enough, he took no particular note of her beauty, which at other times he always did when looking at women. It was as if her beauty were unimportant; later he was to think of this and reflect upon it. Her beauty was self-evident and

23

meant nothing, for she herself was so much more than beauty. Her step was as light as a bird's; she wore thin-soled sandals with a silver loop round the ankle, and walked as if weightless.

This was what he saw. But in a sense he scarcely saw it at all, absorbed as he was in the sensation with which the vision filled him. One should bear in mind the nature of the man; she came as a revelation of something utterly unlike himself, and he was unused to being filled with anything but himself.

Why should this happen to him?

Why should he have been just at this spot when she went past? It was by pure chance. Pure chance brought him outside the Damascus Gate. He knew not why he had gone there; he had had no special reason, and it was not his way to go somewhere without reason.

Why should this happen to him? And what indeed had happened?

He could make nothing of it.

Slowly he took his hand from his eyes and beheld the people passing in front of him, in and out of the Damascus Gate. Strangers, strangers . . .

Abstractedly he walked to the gate and passed through.

He tried to find out who she was, but this was not easy. He was unwilling to give himself away and explain why he wanted to know. And he would not describe her, and reveal the image he had of her to the vile rabble of spies and informers that surrounded him; it would be despicable. They had knowledge of almost everyone in Jerusalem, except the poor, and she could not be one of those. He was repelled by the thought of turning to any of his people. And would he be able to give a clear account of what he had seen?

So it was a long time before he knew anything of the woman he had met.

He went many times to the Damascus Gate, at the same hour as before, to stand and wait for her to pass by.

But she never came.

He thought he would never see her again.

Then by a strange chance he learned who she was; that she had come only recently to Jerusalem, where she was living with kinsfolk, and that so far she was known to very few. Also that she was of the Maccabean line, whose power he had sought to crush by murdering its leaders. She belonged to the ruling class.

One of her relatives, a boy of twelve or thirteen, had tried to stab a palace guard in revenge for cruelties

26

committed upon his people. He had been seized
and thrown into a dungeon until there was time to
deal with him, for by the use of suitable means,
information of some value might be extracted from
him.

It was on this account that on the following day
King Herod, to his amazement, beheld the young
woman from the Damascus Gate being led into his
presence. She walked towards him with her light,
birdlike steps, and was dressed exactly as before.

He gripped the arms of his chair till his knuckles
whitened, but otherwise betrayed nothing of his
feelings.

She had come to intercede for the boy, her kinsman, because of his youth: he was a mere child,
unable to appreciate the enormity of his act.

It was bold of her indeed to enter the presence of
the dreaded monarch, and to beg mercy from such
a man as he. And the sight of her slight and slender
27

figure standing there before him made her courage seem all the more remarkable.

He said as much to her.

She did not understand. What more natural than that she should come to him upon so urgent a matter? Surely no courage was needed for that? Why should she be afraid?

These last words made a peculiar impression upon him, for he had never heard anything like them before.

Someone unafraid of him . . .

He looked at her. He looked at her pale, candid face with its delicate complexion, so much fairer than the common run. But her eyes and lashes were dark, and her gaze also, although it was strangely gentle.

Now for the first time he perceived her beauty, and dwelt upon it.

Her lips were full and slightly pouting, softly pink and not painted like those of the palace

28

women—and of many grand ladies in the city.

From her own mouth he learned who and what she was. She told him unhesitatingly that she, like the young boy, was a Maccabee; and she seemed proud of it. She knew that the Maccabees too had once been kings.

Again he wondered whence she derived her courage. Was it her very fragility that made her so strong and brave?

He met her eyes, though hesitantly, knowing the nature of his own—knowing that people shied away from them.

But she did not. She met his gaze serenely and naturally, altogether untroubled.

"We will send for the lad," he said.

A guard brought him in. He was small and skinny for his age, with coal-black hair and wild black eyes blazing with hatred. At the sight of Herod he seemed ready to fly at him. At her he shot a swift, astonished glance, then never looked at her again.

Herod regarded the boy with an amused little smile, not altogether devoid of menace.

"Why do you do such foolish things?" he asked, ruffling the child's black hair. Then he felt the boy's arm muscles.

"How strong are you?" he added, still smiling. Then to the guard: "Let him go. He won't do it again."

The boy glared at him once more, and then walked unhurriedly and unconcernedly away through the hall. He was wearing only a loincloth, and his small shoulder blades stuck out from his thin back.

❮❮❮-❮❮❮-❮❮❮-

Herod turned to her.

"I have seen you before," he said.

"That is not possible."

"Yes. Outside the Damascus Gate. Flowers grow there. They are very beautiful, but I don't know what they are called. And I never noticed their beauty until you came by."

She made no answer, but laid her slender hand below her belly as if in self-defence. This is said to be the unconscious gesture of women throughout the ages; nor was she herself aware of what she did.

"I went there several times afterwards, hoping that you would pass again—but you never did.

"Now you have come. You have come to *me*. I am glad of it, and glad to see you again. And if I have been able to do a trifle for you, and please you a little, I too am pleased. Should there ever be anything else you wish for, come to me again and I will

31

do what I can. I think I can do anything for you.

"May I then expect to see you again?"

"Yes," she answered hesitantly. For the first time she seemed to have lost her self-assurance.

He noticed this.

They parted then; she walked very quietly away through the great hall, and as quietly all the way home.

How fateful for her was this meeting!

umour spread of this incredible mildness of the tyrant, and of the one who had obtained the boy's release. It was past understanding, yet among the oppressed there awoke a faint hope. Many had husbands or sons or other relatives languishing in Herod's dungeons—that is, if they had not already been executed, or had not perished from ill-treatment, privation, and hunger; but this was something that no one knew. They came to her imploring her help, her intercession.

She was dismayed at what they asked of her, and at their faces, which were more distraught and despairing than any she had ever seen.

Of course she would help them—help them all—if she could. But how? They besieged her with supplications, but had no idea what it would entail for her. How could she tell them?

Nor could she plead on behalf of all of them, for

then Herod would certainly be enraged and show mercy to none. She could not intercede for more than one at a time. She told them so, and explained it to them. Each of them then demanded that this son or that husband should be the chosen one, for such is human nature. It was hard for her to look into all these suffering, tear-stained faces and make but a single choice.

When she had done so she said nothing of it: each supplicant believed that the one she had pleaded for—the one she so longed to see again— was the man chosen.

With a troubled heart their champion walked that weary way to the palace again.

When he saw her he rose and went towards her with a smile that plainly showed his pleasure at her return. He looked at her silently; his gaze was searching, but not hard to meet. There was no lechery in it, as might have been expected from all that was said of him; he seemed merely intent on seeing her truly. Not to desire her, but with a great seriousness and something akin to tenderness. There was nothing frightening about him at all.

Her errand was thus less difficult than she had expected, and without fear she made her plea.

"Is this man also a kinsman of yours?" he asked.

"No, he is not."

He looked at her hard, and then summoned the captain of the prison guard. The captive proved to be a young man who ought to have been sentenced to death. After dismissing the officer, Herod turned to her again.

"What young man is this? Do you know him?"

"No."

"Why then are you so anxious that he should be pardoned?"

"Because his mother begged it of me."

"Ah. His mother."

He looked suspiciously at her.

"Do you really not know him?"

"How could I? I've only just come to Jerusalem."

"Yes," said he, reassured, "that is true."

It was now for the first time that she perceived his suspiciousness, which was a disease in him.

His manner changed; he promised to release the prisoner and they spoke no more of the matter. Instead he showed her over his palace, room by room, all deserted. She was astonished that he should live so, and that there should be so few people about, only a servant here and there. No women, though she had heard there were many. He seemed to be living almost alone in that great palace—apart from the prisoners, of course, and those who guarded them.

36

When they returned to the room where he had received her, he said:

"You must understand that I pardon these criminals merely in order to see you again, and for no other reason. I ought not to do it—I know that very well."

And so they parted.

It was a fact that he had rid the palace of all the women, all the painted whores; and indeed all the shady characters, both men and women, by whom he had been surrounded. He had cleansed his whole house.

He had had no woman since he met her.

She continued to visit him, because all her unfortunate kinsfolk besought her to do so, and because she herself was filled with compassion for those who were pining away in prison. At times he refused her requests, and was adamant; at others she sensed that the one she pleaded for was no longer alive. Yet often she could win mercy from him—from this man who so greatly terrified all others—feeling that by this self-sacrifice she was doing some good. For that it was a sacrifice she could not deny.

Her own people disapproved of these visits to the detested Edomite, who was guilty of the death of many of their nearest kin. She lived with them and was dependent upon them, and found it very hard to endure all they said *at* her, and allowed her to hear. Did she then not know that two of her father's brothers had fallen victim to the infamous tyrant who, with the help of the Romans, had seized the throne, although he was not of the tribe of Judah? Her own father would certainly have shared their fate had he not died a natural death shortly before their murder.

Her bitterest opponent was the young boy, who until then had been devoted to her and had always sought her company. His little face was quite distorted when he reviled her and displayed his contempt. But she looked very gently upon him, and at times laid her hand upon his head to calm him. His behaviour was not to be wondered at, for Herod was said to have cut down and slain the lad's father with his own sword—perhaps the very sword that he always wore about the palace.

But others—those whom she had helped, or those who hoped for her help—were full of thankfulness, and showed it in every way. Their faces when they met her were radiant, and women fell on their knees to kiss the hem of her garment. Such people gave her great joy, and spurred her efforts to soften the heart of that most cruel tyrant. But his heart was not of the kind to be softened; and indeed he had told her that he spared his captives only because it was she who interceded for them, only that he might see her again.

These were hard words. How would she fare along the perilous path upon which she had set her feet?

Her own people rejected and abandoned her, especially the obdurate little boy—he who had flown into her arms when first she came to them, when first he saw her.

It was always with a heavy heart that she approached the palace. A double guard was kept at all the outer doors, and at the main entrance a stronger guard still. Troops were stationed along the whole perimeter of the fortress, armed with swords and other weapons. And he whom they guarded was a lonely man who strayed through deserted rooms, he too bearing a sword because he went in fear of his life; or so it was said.

Would she be able to win something from him this time—from this man who seemed a captive in his own evil stronghold?

One day he asked her to be his wife. He did not say that he loved her: she must have known that for a long time. Nor could he even pronounce the word; he had never used it, and was shy of it. It was no word for him, he felt.

She made no answer, and he demanded none. Think about it, he said—and said it almost submissively.

How swiftly the breath came and went between her pale half-parted lips when she left him! How

41

swiftly she sped through the streets with her bird-like steps and her fluttering heart! Sped? Whither should she speed? She had nothing, no place, to fly to.

She walked more slowly. Slowly and aimlessly. She tried to control herself and to think—to think how to act. There was no one to help her: the decision lay with her alone. But, as she told herself, this was something she was used to. Only now it was far more difficult than ever before.

Should she sacrifice herself to the point of sharing his life? His terrifying life? For herself she could never do it, but only for the sake of others. Could she achieve any good surrendering to him—could she do anything for these poor sufferers who pleaded with her and trusted in her? All those whom he made to suffer?

Such were the questions she put to herself over and over again. Could she gentle his spirit and make his deeds less evil? Could she? Would she be able to change him?

He was repugnant to her; yet she never regarded him as others did. She could not deny that in the course of all her visits to him she had conceived some sort of feeling for this man whom all hated, and rightly hated. She felt sorry for him. And what this implied was hard to say: she would not—and could not—explain it to herself. Compassion came easily to her, and it may be that compassion was what she felt for him. But was it compassion alone?

She knew that she could never love him; but she could feel pity. And in feeling this she felt also the need to sacrifice herself. Should she do this now, for him?

Of love she knew nothing; she believed only that she would sacrifice herself.

Where was she? In which street? It seemed fa-

43

miliar: did it not lead to the Damascus Gate? Yes,
she could see it.

Should she go to it?

She walked up to it; then went further along the
road, and paused. There were no flowers in the
wayside field. One could see that they had once
bloomed there, but they had withered away.

She turned and went home.

After a while she went to the palace and told him
that if he wished it she would be his wife. He was
gladdened by this. It was plain that he was very
happy, although being unused to happiness, he was
unused also to expressing it or showing it.

She gave him her hand. So slender was it, and so
small in his that they both smiled a little, for all
their gravity. There they stood, face to face, as
great a contrast as could well be imagined: she

44

slight and fragile, with the sensitive face inherited from many generations, beautiful as with an ancient beauty; and he with his massive great body, his massive, unhandsome, coarse-featured face.

He did not embrace her. He made no such gesture, no such approach; and for this she was grateful. But afterwards, when she left him, she reflected that it might have been wrong of her to feel thankful for such a thing.

She was of those who continually ask themselves if they have done wrong.

O n the wedding night she was terrified by the violent passion with which he possessed her. She knew nothing of love, and had never imagined that it could be like this. She tried to respond, but never having had a man before she lacked experience in both following and controlling him. Darkness alone prevented him from perceiving this, and from seeing her tormented face.

It was too violent this first time, and too painful, for her to find any pleasure in it. Later she did so, at least now and then. She grew more used to him, and even induced him to be gentler and more considerate with her. Her own instinct now awoke and —despite the great difference between them, or perhaps because of it—she was at times deeply fulfilled. She had to admit this, repugnant though she found him.

Thus their life together turned out better than

she had dared to hope; yet she could never truly accustom herself to him. She feared lest he should discover this, and did all she could to conceal it. She may not always have succeeded, and she knew how suspicious he was. She tried not to think of or dwell upon those qualities in him that repelled her, and in this she was increasingly successful.

But she could not persuade herself that she loved him.

She transformed the palace—or a part of it—into something more nearly resembling a home. She dispelled its desolation, and saw to it that the rooms she chose were habitable and even pleasant: one could see that they were intended for human beings. She never really felt at home there, but at least the rooms were now very different from what they had been before. Some of the vast, bleak halls

47

were left untouched—they meant nothing to her. She never entered them.

What she could never endure was the presence of the captives in the dungeons below. No sound could be heard from them, and they were in no way noticeable—but they were there. She told him that she could not bear the awareness of this, and begged him to lift the burden from her by releasing them. She knew he would never comply for their sake, so she pleaded with him to do it for hers, because she was now his wife and had to live in this fortress of his; she would not live in a prison.

When she had put the matter clearly to him he consented. All the prisoners were released except for certain hardened criminals who were to be executed.

"So they too will be free," he said, gravely and without mockery.

It was indeed a remarkable event, and news of it

ran like wildfire through the city. At first people were sceptical, but the truth of it soon appeared. The many to whom their dear ones were restored blessed the name of Mariamne, the good queen Mariamne who had softened the heart of the wicked king and moved him to this amazing clemency.

Blessed be she. Blessed be she.

But her kinsfolk loathed and detested her for what she had done; for having become the wife of the despised and repulsive usurper. What a disgrace to their lineage, which was of royal blood. What shame. It could never be forgiven, and all communication between them ceased. They could have desired her death, that her disgrace and theirs might be wiped out.

She knew nothing of this, and would not have believed it had she been told.

≪≪≪≪≪

The people, on the other hand—or most of them—
adored her for having had the prisoners released
and because of their hopes for her good influence
on the tyrant. If any change could be brought about
it would be her doing and hers alone. And they
believed her capable of any marvel.

But she was adored for her own sake too; not only
for her charitable deeds but for her nature, and
because she seemed so different from all other people. In this hard and cruel age she was quiet and
gentle, with an inward smile bestowed on everyone
she met, on all whom she looked upon with her
dark-eyed gaze. No sooner did she appear in the
streets than she was loved; love flowed towards her.
She was known to everyone, and recognised at
once, partly because she was always dressed in the
same manner. For although she was now queen she

dressed as before: simply, it seemed, but in fact this was not so. Her garments were often embroidered with silver thread, her mantle was edged with silver, and her girdle or sash too was of silver, as were the loops of her sandals.

The paleness of silver suited her; it suited her kind of beauty, and seemed a part of it. If she wore ornaments, they too were of silver, never of gold. The king, in these early days, longed to heap costly jewellery upon her, set with all the gems of the Orient, skilfully cut for woman's adornment. But she would accept none of it. She would not change just because she had become queen; she wished to remain as she had always been, and to wear— though she gave it little thought—what she had chosen to wear from the beginning.

People loved to see her thus. The eyes of those who met her in the street glowed suddenly when they recognised her bright figure. And the women

51

who fell upon their knees to kiss the hem of her mantle could not have imagined her differently. All loved her as she was.

They called her Mariamne the silver-clad.

One evening when an old serving woman from her kinsmen's house came to visit her secretly in the palace, she learned that the obdurate little boy had moved up into the hills to join a Maccabean band that was quartered there. She wondered whether his flight could have any connection with her marriage to the hated man. She hoped not. Yet every night she imagined him up there in the hills, and beheld his tormented little face.

It was true that she had a good influence on the king. He changed for the better; his rule became milder, his cruelty lessened—or at least became less evident. No one could deny this, or fail to notice it. No one could doubt that it was Mariamne's doing; even those who despised her for marrying the repulsive Edomite acknowledged that.

All but her own family, who remained adamant in their deadly hatred.

He once took her to the temple. He wanted to show it to her, for it was *his*. They walked about in it for a long time, and he explained everything to her, telling her what it would be like and how it would be even more beautiful than Solomon's.

She listened, but appeared to care little for what she saw. It seemed to have no appeal for her. Perhaps she felt no need of a temple.

She was in fact a very selfless person, unlike him, who had built this sanctuary for himself. She was

withdrawn into herself, certainly, and dwelt there,
but in quite a different way from him. Perhaps she
was not really religious, or if she was then it was unawares, as if she were good without being conscious
of it or giving it a thought. Could it have been so?

Did she need no temple?

He never took her with him on his nocturnal wanderings about the temple, but walked there alone in
the darkness.

Why did he do it? He himself could not have
said: there was no object in it. And yet he went
there, and walked for a long time in the darkness.
Then he would stand outside for a while, looking
up at the fiery night sky.

He had no link with the divine. Inwardly he was
a wilderness, and the stars drove their cold spears
into his soul.

He kept a part of his life to himself, and would not allow her to know of it. Not only such things as the nocturnal walks about his temple, but other matters as well. He was unused to having a confidant and she never became one. They did not confide in each other: it would have suited neither of them.

She too was accustomed to determining her own way of life, and he allowed her to do so. They minded their own affairs, without interference from each other.

But he knew far more of her doings than she knew of his. Being suspicious by nature, he was exceedingly observant; he also had an efficient intelligence service.

Thus, for example, he was well aware that the old serving woman from the house of her Maccabean kinsfolk had been to see her.

55

If she had known this, she would have been very uneasy.

He was incensed that the boy whom he had released should have gone up to one of the Maccabean haunts in the hills. He had been a fool to release him, and ought never to have done it. His anger persisted, although the matter was of no importance.

But to Mariamne he said nothing.

His violent desire for her was undiminished. She found it hard to satisfy, so demanding was he. His virility seemed inexhaustible, while her need of tenderness was too deep for him to satisfy. She had tried to make him a little gentler and more considerate, and had even succeeded at times, but not

56

always. He still thought chiefly of himself, and was too violent in love, as in everything else; sometimes she felt as if his heavy body would stifle her.

He had never had such a woman, and this may have accounted for his passion. She was new to him, and his very opposite; and from this arose also his inability to understand her, or to enter into her alien, cool, emotional world.

He had never experienced love before, and knew nothing about it. It was foreign to his nature. He knew that he loved her, but did not know what this should imply. And love wrought no change in him.

But his desire for her he did understand; he believed it to be enough, he believed it to be love.

Often she was too exhausted to feel anything, yet she did her best to respond and to satisfy him; partly because she feared to deny him anything, and partly because she wanted him to find release

57

with her—release from his lust, his immoderate desires.

Afterwards, when she stroked his forehead, he lay still, and she seemed to have brought tranquillity to that massive creature. She was glad to know that she had done this, for in a way she was fond of him—she pitied him and was just a little fond of him.

How wicked was he really? Surely not so wicked as before?

He had never behaved wickedly to her; but she wanted him to be good to everyone.

It was inevitable that in time he should begin to notice the strained nature of her love for him, and realise that she did not feel as he did. With other women he had been indifferent to this, so long as he himself was satisfied; but it was not so with her.

58

It troubled him, though he kept his feelings to himself, as he always did. It was not easy for such a man
to endure a like humiliation, and never would he reveal it.

There was no doubt that it did trouble him. He
brooded, and grew sombre, and his look frightened
her; she dared not meet it. And he avoided looking
at her, and although she knew the reason she dared
not speak of it to him. What could she have said?
It is never easy for two living together to mention
such things, and with their utter lack of candour it
was impossible. She strove even harder to please
him and to show him that not only did he need her;
she too needed him. But this merely strengthened
his suspicions and his vigilant observation of her,
making all plainer to him and more fateful for them
both.

The silence between them deepened, and he
tried with all his might to conceal his need of her,

59

though it was hard to force himself to this. At last he no longer approached her, and made no demands.

It was in this way that he showed his love for her.

Fighting in the hills had flared up once more. Few in Jerusalem were aware of it, apart from those who were in communication with the Maccabean forces. Herod, of course, who received messengers from all over the country, was informed of it and knew where the fighting had begun. It was not his own people who had started it this time; they had been set upon by the Maccabees. His troops were said to be few in that area just now, which was why the enemy had attacked.

Messengers coming and going at the palace showed that something was afoot, and Mariamne could not fail to notice it. She was not surprised therefore when Herod told her he must leave Jerusalem for a while, as his presence was needed elsewhere. Just where he did not say. They bade each other farewell, and she held his hand linger-ingly in both of hers—in her cool hands.

As always he felt it a relief to get away from the palace and from Jerusalem, and perhaps now more than ever.

When he and his suite and the reinforcements he took with him drew near the hills, and he felt the cool winds that blew from them, he became him-self again, his old self, the son of his fathers, despite the brooding gloom within him which left him no peace.

He alone was mounted; he rode by himself ahead of bodyguard and troops. But they were used to this; he never mixed with either officers or men.

61

Yet he was popular with them because he let them do as they pleased, and plunder and rob to their hearts' content. They liked him too just because he did keep aloof—that was the kind of leader, the kind of army commander they preferred. He was not one of them, and ought not to be.

It was long since he had campaigned with them, and they were glad to see him among them again. But they noticed that he was in an unusually sombre mood.

On coming up into the hills they made contact with one of their pickets in the hollow road that they were following and learned where the troops were stationed. They came upon them in an upper valley. Campfires had been lit, for it was cold at this height and at this season. The commanding officer was surprised by the unexpected visit, for although he had asked for reinforcements he had not supposed that Herod himself would come with them.

He made his report upon all that had taken place since the fighting began, and Herod, having listened in silence, criticised much of what had been done. When the general defended his actions by saying that his forces were inadequate, the king replied that those forces would have sufficed if properly used. He was displeased, and showed it. The officer, an elderly man and long accustomed to his lord and his sometimes difficult moods, perceived that something was amiss and that Herod's judgment was at fault. Herod knew too much about these hill battles and the difficulties they entailed to comment in this way without some special cause.

While they were talking a scout dashed down the hill, shouting when still at a distance that the enemy were advancing through the narrow pass to the east. This pass formed the only entrance to the valley.

Herod at once took over command and issued

rapid orders. He wanted to meet the enemy in the pass itself if he could. But before the troops had formed up and the reinforcements had taken their proper positions among them, the Maccabees had forced their way into the eastern end of the valley and deployed there. But they were halted by Herod's men, and soon the battle was at its height, with war cries ringing out from both sides.

The Maccabees knew nothing of the reserves that had been brought up and were astonished at the strength of the opposition. But they fought with all the fanatical savagery and contempt for death for which they were famous. Had Herod not come up in support with his fresh, well-rested troops, nothing could have withstood them, and the whole of his army might have been annihilated, confined as it was in this valley. Now the outcome was very different: the assailants found themselves counter-attacked by seemingly limitless numbers. Casualties

64

on both sides were considerable, but far more disastrous for the Maccabees, who were now numerically inferior.

Herod himself fought in the forefront as always, though apparently without his usual zest. If anyone delighted in battle it was he, yet now he seemed listless and ill-humoured. He fought like an ordinary soldier, without the fury that usually distinguished him.

The battle took its inevitable course. The Maccabees, for all their valour, had lost so many men and their struggles were so futile that they perceived it themselves, though they were unwilling to yield.

In the final stage of the conflict a skinny little boy appeared among the Maccabees, armed with a sword which was indeed smaller than theirs, but still too big and heavy for him. It was a strange sight.

Even stranger was it when Herod, catching sight
of the lad, dashed straight at him and cut savagely
down through his left shoulder and breast to the
heart.

Those near him wondered at the violent slaying
of the boy, who was no more than a child, and no fit
opponent for Herod. Yet of course the youngster
had taken up arms like the rest, and like them had
to run the risk of death. He looked very pitiful
when dead—thin-cheeked, and with blood all over
his body, though not on his face. How curious that
they should number children among their troops;
they had surely never done so before.

Afterwards Herod seemed excited, and breathed
heavily. He threw one swift glance at the prostrate
boy, and never looked that way again.

By the time this happened the battle was really
over. A great number of the Maccabees had withdrawn through the pass, and only a minor force re-

mained to cover the retreat. These too then took to flight.

The bodies lay on the field of battle where they had suffered defeat, the boy's among them.

Herod's men tended their own wounded, but left those of the enemy lying where they were, for such had always been the custom on both sides. Then they withdrew to their camp and gathered about their fires.

The day was ending. The men sat down and cleaned their weapons. Herod too cleaned his sword.

Dusk fell.

ariamne heard of it through a Maccabee who had witnessed the incident, and who had later ventured down into Jerusalem to have his wounds dressed. But the one who actually told her was the old serving woman from her kinsfolk's house.

She wept for two days.

t was long before Herod came back to Jerusalem. No doubt he was reluctant to return. But Mariamne was unconscious of time; she merely mourned her little kinsman's death, and the manner of it. Being what she was, she could not understand. For days on end she would sit staring before her with empty eyes, trying to grasp what had happened, and why. Always, always she beheld that hard little boy, who had run straight into her arms when first he saw her—when first she entered his home.

His face was pale, his look reproachful—or so it seemed to her.

Was she to blame for his death? For his flight into the hills, and thus for his death? Was it because she had become the wife of Herod the hated? Had this so appalled him that he had fled?

Such were her brooding thoughts.

She wondered for what reason Herod had slain

him, and why in the brutal way described to her, for this was past all understanding. Was it because Herod forgave no one—not even a child? Such was his nature, she knew; at times he even admitted as much. He might have regretted his clemency in releasing the lad, and been angered to find him among the enemy bands in the hills.

She was no less guilty on that account. However it might be, it was she who was to blame.

And perhaps—perhaps . . . But no, it was surely not possible . . .

Surely Herod's act could not be one of revenge because she did not love him? Or not enough—not as a man desires to be loved.

Surely, surely this could not be so?

If it were, she was guilty in a way that . . .

She was baffled. Baffled.

But she was of those who blame themselves for everything.

≪≪≪≪≪≪

When at last Herod returned to Jerusalem he saw at once that Mariamne knew. Her face was transformed by sorrow, yet strangely enough in a manner that made her seem lovelier than before. It was paler, almost transparent, illuminated from within by grief.

She had no tears left. For a long while now her eyes had lost their capacity for weeping, though they were filled with the sorrow for which she had wept. They seemed still moist from the tears that they had shed; and strangely enough were all the gentler for it, all the warmer, whereas the eyes of others would surely have been hardened by suffering. But in her, suffering seemed to have brought with it an even greater gentleness.

When Herod beheld her and perceived what he had done to her—perceived how much she had

71

borne on his account—he fell down at her feet with a groan, and the sweat of anguish broke out upon his forehead. He held up his arms, but without touching her, and looked at her imploringly with bloodshot eyes. Wordlessly he begged forgiveness for his wickedness, for being what he was. Forgiveness from her who could forgive everything.

And with her cool hand she stroked his forehead, wiping the sweat of anguish from that brutal brow and from the damp, blackish-red hair, until his lips ceased to quiver, his eyes lost something of their wildness and savagery, and he seemed to find a kind of peace.

S he let him weep himself out beside her; she let him come to her to still his trouble and his lust. She tried to be as she had always been, hard though this was. For thus, she thought, she might retain some little part of her influence over him; and to do this it was with her that she must let him find solace. It was also true that she needed him, though she tried not to think of this. He had roused her senses, and once aroused they craved their part in her life—but not as his craved it. She could not respond to him in his way at all.

She was astonished that after what had happened she could take the smallest pleasure with him; and yet she did. She reproached herself for this, as for everything else. And in the darkness she beheld the pale face of the little boy with the sorrowful eyes, which had grown even larger now that he was dead.

For a while Herod was calmer. This much she

had achieved. And in Jerusalem at least there was
no word of any exceptional atrocities, so far as she
knew. But she had little contact with the outside
world. For this she depended mainly on the oc-
casional visits of the old serving woman. This
woman came without the knowledge of the family,
for had they known of it they would have been in-
dignant and she herself in some danger. Nevertheless she came. For though she said no word of it,
she had grown attached to Mariamne during her
brief sojourn in their house, and Mariamne to her.
The face of the old woman was furrowed and stern,
though she was certainly less stern than she appeared. It was simply that she never smiled. Why
this should be was unknown. But some people
never do smile, especially old people who have
traversed the whole of life.

She talked a little of what had happened in the
kinsfolk's house, and of what they said about events

74

in Jerusalem and in the countryside. She was taciturn by nature, and she came not so much to talk as to sit for a little while with Mariamne.

Mariamne was very glad of it, and thankful to her for coming, partly for the pleasure of seeing her again and partly because it kept her in some slight touch with the world and enabled her to ask after her family, of whom she was very fond. They were said to detest her, but that she would not believe.

She continued her strolls about the city and often went beyond it. It was unusual for women to walk abroad, but to her it was natural and customary, for she had been born not in Jerusalem but in quite a small town belonging to her family, no longer there. Nor did the town itself now exist. When last she had beheld it, it lay in smoking ruins.

During these walks of hers she met many people, but they were strangers to her and she had little

75

contact with them. Yet they often recognised her and smiled at her, perhaps because she had at some time helped a member of their family. And the recent changes which led men to believe that they were living in a gentler age were attributed entirely to her. Therefore they smiled at her whenever they saw and recognised her, and many continued to kneel and kiss the hem of her mantle.

Mariamne the silver-clad.

Yet they wondered at the alteration in her. What could be the reason?

They wondered why she no longer smiled at them.

either the improved conditions in the country nor the calmer relationship between the two in the palace could endure forever.

Herod grew restless again—or perhaps one should say more like himself. He slid away into his own shut-away, suspicious world, and she saw clearly that she had lost her power over him.

She knew why—and this time he told her himself.

At last he went to war again, up into the hills where he was always happiest.

Mariamne grieved little at this, for of late her life had become still more burdensome. He had begun to reproach her openly with her lack of love for him, speaking of it continually. Until then he had striven to conceal his humiliation, as he called it; he had refused to acknowledge it, and kept it to himself. But now he spoke out freely, to her face, saying he

knew very well that she did not love him, and that
he noticed it every time they came together; that
she knew it too and showed it all too plainly,
especially by pretending to long for him, pretending to be full of desire when she felt none; pretending a kind of fire and heat that her cool body—
her pale, suffering body where all was cold: hands,
belly, heart and all—could never know.

She regarded him with her sorrowful dark eyes,
and when he could no longer endure that candid
gaze he flung away from her, his own eyes savage
and bloodshot as he threw himself down upon a
bench in another room, his heart pounding in his
breast.

Thus, before he went up into the hills, they
parted.

or Mariamne in her solitude there followed a time of quietness. She began to live as herself, something she had not done for a long time. She sank into herself, into her own essence, though with no trace of self-centredness. She lived, she truly existed; and something—she knew not what—passed through her soul and her cool, fragile body like a breeze through a tree.

She had little knowledge of herself. For so unusual and even singular a person it was odd how unaware she was of her own nature and how little she cared about it—or rather, would have cared about it had she ever given it a thought.

She was indeed like a tree, which has no consciousness of itself, and is a secret. A great secret, perhaps. Yet the tree knows nothing of this: it is a secret even from itself.

One may wonder why it was that she needed no

temple; but neither do trees, flowers, and the beautiful stones to be found along the shore.

She was like the trees. The wind is the worship that fills them, and to which at times—though not always—they listen. Their divine service is within themselves.

It may have been this to which she listened during those still and solitary days.

She walked through that part of the palace which she had tried to turn into a home. It had little likeness to a real home; no one could have denied that. Her true home no longer existed; it had been in a little town that now lay in ruins—a light, happy home, and she recalled it with joy.

She remembered her mother and father and her two brothers. All of them were gone. She still had her kinsfolk in Jerusalem, of course, though it was said that they hated her. Nevertheless they were hers, so she was not utterly alone.

From time to time the old serving woman came to
see her, and talked of them but never of their hatred; she never mentioned that. Nor did she speak
any ill of Herod, although she must have known a
great deal about him. Indeed she spoke no evil of
anyone. Yet she came more often during his
absence.

Once when Mariamne was walking in the city she
came to a well where women were drawing water.
The well was in a little square, and women must
have fetched water from it for ages past. Both
square and well were very ancient, like everything
else in Jerusalem.

As she now passed by she noticed that one of the
women was a near kinswoman, a cousin of her own
age. She hastened towards her with arms out-
stretched, her lips parted to speak her name. But

81

the young woman turned away and, her jar being already filled, departed, bearing it upon her head, along the narrow street leading to her home. And she did not look back.

Mariamne watched her go.

When Herod came back he was in a dark mood. He avoided her, and when she asked how he had fared in the hills he replied that all had gone well and that many of her rebellious race had lost their lives, if that was what she meant.

On a later occasion he mentioned in passing that he had had other women up there: camp followers and Maccabean captives. These were entirely different from her, albeit of the same race.

Mariamne made no reply.

He was annoyed that she did not answer—that she seemed not to care. But he showed nothing of this.

82

He was not only resentful; he was disappointed too. He had expected her to be outraged by what he told her.

That he had been disgusted by these women was something he did not mention. He refused to admit it even to himself.

And it was not only disgust that he had felt, for—perhaps for that very reason—they satisfied him too. They were so unlike Mariamne, whom he loved.

There was sensual delight in experiencing something so different from her and her purity. Too great a purity can become wearisome.

But it was she whom he loved.

As for her silence: certainly she was hurt that he had taken other women, certainly she was troubled, but she had expected nothing else. She could not reproach him.

He never sought her now; he never came near

her, and this grieved her, for she could not truth-
fully deny that she missed the sensual satisfaction
to which he had accustomed her, in spite of so
much in him that revolted and disgusted her.

She reflected that his recourse to women might
be a token of a reversion to his old way of life, and
this made her very uneasy. Clearly she had lost all
power over him, so what would happen now?

It soon appeared that her anxiety was well-
founded.

Rumours arose of a sterner regime, sterner times;
of men who had been seized, or had vanished, who
had been dragged from their homes and families
and never afterwards heard of. Once more terror
spread through Jerusalem.

The prison cells in the palace filled again; what
went on in them was unknown, but might be

guessed. Mariamne lived from day to day in dread
and sorrow, hardly knowing how to endure. She
feared also for her kinsfolk. Their house too might
have been forced, like so many others. This was not
so, as she later heard, but only because no men remained in it. Only women were left.

Things happened at the palace too. Herod had
grown used to a different sort of woman, and more
of them, such as he had possessed in earlier days,
and his courtiers arranged for painted whores and
courtesans to come once more to the palace. Herod
took them not from lust alone, but in order to
humiliate, wound, and degrade her whom he loved
and who did not love him; he did it from sheer mal-
ice. For in him love itself was evil.

But it was not easy to degrade Mariamne. There
was something in and about her—something not to
be explained—which kept her aloof. She walked
through that house of vice as if untouched by her

85

surroundings. They affected her, of course, but she
felt no humiliation or degradation, being incapable
of them.

Once he assailed her with furious reproaches for
putting up with it, for not caring about what was
going on all round her or upbraiding him for his
vicious life. Why didn't she? How could she help
it? How . . .

But he broke off his ravings abruptly and averted
his bloodshot eyes, and she had no need to answer.

He left her, and it was to be long before they met
again. Indeed it could be said that this was the last
time they ever saw each other, unless one counts
the day he came to her when she was dying, when
she was nearly dead because he came too late.

That day still lay in the future, but from now on
they avoided one another.

❮❮❮❮❮❮❮❮❮

Mariamne and those other women remained on good terms. They were not to blame for anything, and gave her no reason to complain; and she gave them none. In return they showed consideration for her; perhaps they too were impressed by her nature; perhaps they were sorry for her, and felt more pity for her than for themselves.

They lived elsewhere in the palace, while she remained in the rooms which she had turned into a sort of home. She was always allowed to keep these rooms for herself.

Only one of the women, a captured Maccabean who owed her presence there to a certain coarse-limbed beauty, poured forth her measureless hatred and contempt upon Mariamne at a chance encounter with her.

"I am a captive," she screamed, "forced to give myself to him, that filthy tyrant, that repulsive Edomite. But you gave yourself of your own free

87

will, and were made queen for it, and think you're very grand. I'm no queen! I'm a raped enemy, and can be proud of it. But what have you to be proud of—can you tell me that? Pah!"

Herod heard from the other women of this one's behaviour to Mariamne, and punished her himself with all the violence of his wrath. She uttered not a sound. Yet he kept her on in the palace, though everyone thought he should not. He liked the way she never resigned herself to her fate, never yielded, so that he always had to take her by force.

Thus, in spite of everything, he would allow no one to insult Mariamne.

The old serving woman had not called for a long while, and Mariamne wondered why. It might mean nothing, for sometimes there were long intervals between her visits. She'll come, Mariamne thought. She'll come soon.

But she did not come.

Weeks had now passed, and Mariamne was really uneasy. What could be the matter? And whom could she ask?

Had the family found out about the visits, and forbidden them? Or what could it be?

She learned at last from one of the palace whores that the old woman who used to come had disappeared, so it was useless to expect her.

Mariamne was much distressed, and asked her how she knew this. She had just heard it, the woman answered.

Did she mean that the old servant was dead? She was not certain, but at any rate she was gone, and death was the most likely explanation.

Mariamne had confirmation of this from another quarter: the woman had been removed because

Herod suspected her of carrying messages between Mariamne and the Maccabees, to whom her family belonged. This meant that he suspected Mariamne herself of being in communication with his enemies.

This was madness, and she could make nothing of it. He could not possibly believe such a thing.

She found it hard, too, to realize that the old woman was dead. She mourned her deeply, for she had been very fond of her—though had she ever told her so? She could not believe there would be no more meetings; the woman had been the only friend she had left, and now she was utterly alone.

She thought of her all day long, remembering her furrowed old face that looked so stern, though she had not been stern. No, not stern. It was just that she never smiled, though no one knew why this was.

And now she was gone.

It was indeed true that he suspected her of communicating with the Maccabees, his foes. The old woman's many visits had aroused his suspicions, and he had had her removed.

Yet the danger was not over, he told himself.

Like many violent men, he was much afraid of death. Although he had caused many others to die, he was terrified of dying. Not in battle—not in the excitement of battle—but he dreaded death from illness, death from within; he dreaded to be bereft of life by an unseen, unknown enemy. Or to be assassinated, to be struck down from behind with a stab under the shoulder blade—the left shoulder blade. It could happen. It might happen at any time.

If there should be a plot to kill him—if—how greatly prized by the conspirators would be an ally

91

so near to him, so unsuspected; near him always, in his own house. Should he not consider this?

Did he believe it? Did he truly believe it? It was not possible. He was suspicious by nature, but surely not to the point of believing that Mariamne sought his life, that she could be implicated in such a plot? Such a thing was unthinkable!

Yet he thought it.

He was careful to conceal from himself what lay behind his growing obsession. Even less did he know—or rather, admit to himself—the dark impulses now stirring in his soul, in the slimy bed of his soul.

Mariamne was still as dearly loved by the people— or by most of them. When she walked through the streets, which she did less often now, they showed their love for her, although she could no longer do

92

anything for them, or exert any influence on their behalf. They loved her although she never smiled at them, and would never smile at them again. They knew of her burden, they knew why she looked so sorrowful—they knew it all. They knew why she had changed and become quite unlike her old self. Yet they loved her.

Mariamne the silver-clad.

He was now trying to make up his mind whether he could any longer endure her being alive—endure her not being dead. It was hard for him, but he had come to a final decision.

It was long since he had seen her. He began to regard her almost as a stranger: a strange woman who was constantly near him, in his own house. He had to think about this. Because although he never saw her, she was continually there, and he must not forget it. She might be in permanent contact with his enemies. He must decide; he could put it off no longer. Not for a day—not for a single day. He must make up his mind.

This was all the easier for him in that he had not seen her for so long.

He hired a man to murder her. He felt easier in his mind when he had arranged this, and spoken to the man.

He felt calmer now that he had at last made his decision.

The assassin was a fellow he had often employed before, for similar tasks. Similar? Similar?

He was a big, tall man like himself. Why? Why

choose one resembling himself? There were plenty
of others, so why this man—this man who was so
like himself?

He rode out a long way beyond Jerusalem. He rode
slowly, for he had no destination. It was a fine day,
a fine, cloudless autumn day; the air was clear, the
sky pure. It could be seen by the sun what hour it
was, and he often looked up at the sky.

For no apparent reason he turned his horse and
rode back towards Jerusalem. After a while—not at
first, but after a while—he increased his pace. Not
much, but he did go faster. And when he drew near
the city he rode really fast, urging his mount with
all his might.

On reaching the palace, the palace gate, he threw
down the reins, let the horse go, and hastened up
the stairs.

95

《《-《《-《《

When he entered her room he found her lying there in her blood, with two stab wounds, one in the breast and the other in the throat. She was still alive, and breathing almost imperceptibly. Her eyes were closed, but on becoming aware of his presence she opened them and looked at him.

"Beloved, beloved," he whispered, bending over her. "Beloved, beloved . . ."

Did she hear him? He would never know.

She could not speak, and made a helpless gesture with her hand. Then laid it in his—her slender little hand in his.

Did she not know? Did she not know? Or did she know, and yet did this?

He sank down; he knelt there not knowing what to do—what in the world to do.

"Beloved" was all he could say.

She shut her eyes again. She drew a deeper breath, and was dead. He saw that she was dead.

He bent over her.

"Beloved, beloved," he repeated over and over again.

But she did not hear.

It was some time, though not very long, before he found her murderer. He rushed upon him in the wildest fury and stabbed him with countless maniacal stabs until the whole of that big body was full of wounds.

Although the man was as big and strong as himself, he made not the smallest resistance, but allowed himself to be cut down.

O f Herod's life after the death of Mariamne, it only remains to be told that he continued exactly as before, in wickedness and cruelty, and that there was no change in his ways. Just as love had failed to alter him, so did Mariamne's death. For a little while, immediately after it, he seemed somewhat milder in mood, and the people felt that they were leading an easier life. Thus for the last time Mariamne had achieved something on their behalf. Then the old ways returned and he was himself again.

Indeed one may say that his wickedness and cruelty increased the longer he lived, and his vainglory, and his belief that he was the mightiest man alive, with none to equal him.

Even his power increased: he succeeded in crushing the Maccabean resistance by inflicting a resounding defeat on their forces in the hills and then exterminating them—or at least all those of any standing. By a continued reign of terror he ruled unchecked over a cowed people.

He continued in his dissolute ways, and at last undermined his health with excesses of all kinds. But he was not broken by them, except physically and by degrees: he remained what he had always been, just as indomitable and dangerous to all about him and to all who dared to incur his hatred or even displeasure. Strength remained to him, as it remained in the loathing that was felt for him.

Nevertheless he was now an old man, and he began to show it. An aged man with but a short time left. Yet he pursued his violence unchanged, satisfying his lusts and passions as always in the past.

But Mariamne he never forgot.

Once when visiting his temple, which had long
stood complete in all its glory, he remembered the
time when he had entered it with Mariamne. He
recalled how little she seemed to care about it—her
indifference. It was strange. As if she had no need
of any temple.

Curious, he thought.

He began to walk about in his temple, in this holy
place which he had built to his own glory, that his
name might pass down to posterity and he himself
become immortal. A place so beautiful, so costly—
perhaps more beautiful than any other temple in
the world. He rejoiced yet again at its gold and
copper, its bronze and silver, and at its gleaming
marble which he had brought at such great ex-
pense from a foreign land. He moved about with his
heavy tread, which had grown even heavier with
age. He looked sick and old; but this was of no con-
sequence, for there was none to see him; he walked

there quite alone. And when he had walked there for a long time and assured himself that all was as it should be, he returned to the palace, to that part of it which Mariamne had made into a home. When alone he always lived there, and that was often, for he was easily bored and repelled by the people he gathered about him.

It was true that Mariamne needed no temple. Her worship was within her, and she could listen to it at any time. She was like a tree which the wind fills with its secret soughing. She had no need of any sanctuary.

But Herod had need of a temple, for he was a desert man. And in the desert he raised a temple over himself.

Over himself only? Only to glorify himself?

That I cannot say. I don't know.

«‹-«‹-«‹-

When his illness worsened and he began to suffer hideous pain, he moved down to the land of his fathers, to the desert country south of the Dead Sea, to seek relief and healing at the hot springs there, which were said to restore health and renew life.

He had never been there before, and he looked with wonder at the country whence his soul had come: the desolate expanses and bleak, blood-red hills. It was a land that terrified, yet filled the soul with a wild joy. But Herod was now too sick and old to appreciate it to the full.

His body found no health there; the sulphur-yellow waters of the hot springs brought him no relief from his pain; they intensified it and burned him like fire. It was a land of death rather than life.

His sickness worsened.

He returned to Jerusalem in a miserable state.
His swollen body was a torment to himself and
others because of its revolting smell. Disease ex-
acerbated his ill temper; his savagery struck at
everything and everyone about him, so that at last
hardly anybody dared approach him. Even his old
servants were afraid to come near.

His sufferings were terrible. He was faced with
what he had feared most of all: having to die from
within, to be bereft of life by an enemy he could not
see and did not know.

And despite his agonies, from which death alone
could release him, the terror of death dogged him
day and night, especially at night. He dreaded the
night.

Illness and terror, however, did not prevent him
from being absorbed in himself, in his greatness,
his superhumanity, as he had been all his life. He
felt outraged that such as he should have to perish

103

like any ordinary mortal, and in the most repulsive manner. He ought to have died the death of a god, but he did not.

The nature of his illness is unknown. He was said to be consumed by worms, whatever that may mean, because of his great wickedness. People did not find this hard to believe.

He lived almost alone in his fortress, for people were as repugnant to him as he to them. Only a few servants remained. But a strongly armed guard stood on duty outside the palace as usual, to watch over his life. His life was very well protected and defended, although everyone hoped for his death.

t happened about this time that a star of greater brilliance than any other appeared in the east. Three wise men from that distant desert country beheld this star, and understanding its message, set forth to follow it. And it stopped over Judea. And when they reached Jerusalem they found their way to the palace and said to the servant who opened to them:

"A royal child has been born—a child who shall be lord over all the earth. If this is the king's palace, it is here that the child must be."

The servant was alarmed, and bade them wait outside while he spoke to his master. It was in great fear that he told Herod of their strange words, for by now anything that happened aroused the king's wrath.

But Herod was not wrathful. To the servant's astonishment—for he had never seen such a thing in his master before—the king seemed almost afraid. At Herod's order he hastened to fetch the three men and bring them before him.

Herod was indeed afraid, but when the three men approached him he regained his calm, for they were too poorly dressed to be the bearers of any important message. However, he asked them why they had come, on what errand. And they repeated the words they had spoken to the servant: that a child had been born who would be king of Judea and of all the world as well.

Herod asked how they knew this.

They replied that they had seen a star kindled in the east, a mighty star which could only betoken the birth of a king; that they had followed this star, and that it had halted over Jerusalem, which must mean that the child had been born here.

Herod smiled to himself at their simplicity, and told them that no child had been born in his palace, so there could be no question of any new prince.

The three men looked at each other in bewilderment, and could make no answer.

But since Herod desired to see the star for himself, it was agreed that they should return late that night, when it would be clearly visible.

When they went back in the evening they climbed to the roof of the palace, whence the star and the whole arc of heaven could best be seen. And they showed the star to Herod.

With his ravaged old face upturned to the night sky he stood and gazed. Certainly this star shone with unusual brilliance. Yet more extraordinary than this, it seemed to him, was the vast starry sky that opened above him, above the royal stronghold, over all Judea, over all the earth. The star was but a small part of the great whole—and it would soon fade and die. But the starry sky itself, in all its desolation, would never fade.

Such was his inward thought.

But the wise men saw that the star was moving, advancing; that it had not halted yet, as they had supposed. So they departed in haste and set forth into the darkness, to follow it once more.

But Herod stood, still gazing up into the mighty vault of heaven, and the stars drove their cold spears into his soul.

When the wise men had walked long through the Judean night they came to a little town whose name was unknown to them. Above this place the star stood still. Above a cave at the edge of the town, where shepherds used to fold their flocks. But a man and a woman and her child were living here now, and it was above this child that the star came to rest. Then it faded from the sky and was seen no more, for it was morning.

The three men then knew that they had reached

their goal: that the child was the king whom they sought, to whom the star was to lead them.

They approached in reverence, and when they reached the entrance to the cave they knelt, and remained kneeling as if in adoration, in their threadbare, faded old mantles, but without expressing their worship in any words. The baby had just woken up because of the morning sun that had begun to shine in, and he looked at them with his clear eyes.

Then they held forth the gifts that they had brought for him.

Since they were very poor and their homeland was desert, their gifts were modest indeed—though neither trivial nor meaningless on that account— and they offered them in all humility.

The first man gave the baby a little stone—a very beautiful stone polished to perfect smoothness on the shore of his own country, which was a desert land by the sea.

109

The second offered a thistle shaped like a sceptre
—a royal sceptre—which had sprung up through
the desert sand far away in his own country.

The third man held forth a small jar containing
water from a spring in his native desert—a spring
which was beyond doubt miraculous, since it welled
forth from the very sand.

Such were the gifts they brought to the baby.

And the parents—good, simple people who had
never been spoilt by costly presents—thanked the
givers very warmly.

And when the men had bowed down once more
before the child, and before its father and mother,
they departed thence and returned to their own
country.

But when it was rumoured to Herod that the baby
of whom the three wise men had spoken had been

born in that little town, he commanded that all male children there and thereabouts should be put to death, that no king might arise from among them.

Impossible, of course, that any king could be born in such a manner; yet for safety's sake he issued the decree.

It might be supposed that a man as old and as ill as he was—almost at the point of death, indeed—would weary of ill-doing and feel indifference as to his successor. But it was not so. There should be no other king but Herod! No other king in all the world! Hence this command—the most hideous of any he had given.

It was his last evil deed, for now his own death was near.

But when the massacre took place in that little town, the child and its father and mother were no longer there.

111

erod was now entirely alone in the palace. The last of the servants had gone: they could stand no more of it. And knowing him to be at the point of death they were no longer afraid of him, no longer afraid to forsake him and go their way.

In this utter solitude he began to think of Mariamne. He had done this often—very often. Never had he forgotten her: she was the only one he had ever loved. Strange that this love could have lived on throughout his long and evil life; yet it had. How it endured alongside his wickedness was past understanding. Yet so it was.

And it had done so without influencing his life, or changing it in any way.

Not even her death had altered him or his way of life. Nor his awareness of his own guilt—for it was he who had killed her, although he had hired another man, one very like himself, to do the deed and so spare him.

Nothing had changed him. Nothing could ever change him.

For he was a desert man. And in his desert there was no miraculous spring of cool, clear water where one could fill a little jar to revive oneself, to be renewed.

No such thing existed for him.

Nor was he like Mariamne, who needed no temple, who was like a tree filled by the wind with its secret soughing. He was not like her.

There was nothing of this in him.

He was himself. He was Herod. Herod the Great.

And now he was to die.

Alone and forsaken, he was to die, like the rest of us. For in death we are all alone, all forsaken. Now he was to die, as we all do.

And it was at night, the time he so deeply dreaded.

So weakened was he by sickness that he could barely stand, but he would not die lying down. He would not. It was not thus that he, Herod, should die.

When he felt his hour approaching he rose and staggered forward, and leaned against the wall. Dying, he dragged his ponderous, swollen body through the palace, through the deserted rooms.

But his only thought was with her whom he had loved. At the hour of his death he thought of her, longed for her still.

"Mariamne! Mariamne!" he cried with a loud voice.

The empty rooms resounded with his cry.

Reeling, propping himself with his hand against the wall he shouted again and again:

"Mariamne! Mariamne!"

And echo repeated hollowly the name of his dead beloved.

In the darkness he dragged himself along, and took the last steps in his evil life.

At last he sank down. He tried to rise, but could not. Stretching out his arms into the darkness before him he cried out for the last time the name of his beloved.

"Mariamne! Mariamne!"

Then his arms dropped limply down and he was dead.

Thus did Herod the great king live out his life here on earth, the time allotted to him. An emblem of mankind: mankind that replenishes the earth but whose race shall one day be erased from it and, so far as may be conjectured, will leave no memorial. Thus he lived his life.

Mariamne. Mariamne.

A Note About the Author

*PÄR LAGERKVIST, an Immortal of the Swedish Academy
since 1940 and Nobel Prize laureate of 1951, was born in 1891 in a
small provincial town in southern Sweden. He lived abroad for years,
in Denmark, Italy, and France, where in 1913 the new Expressionist art
profoundly influenced his thinking and his literary style, making him
turn from naturalism toward a powerful simplicity and purity of ex-
pression. Of his nearly forty published books of poetry, plays, essays, and
fiction,* The Dwarf *(1944) was the first to gain him international fame,
while* Barabbas *(1951) is perhaps the most widely known, having been
made into a film by Dino de Laurentiis. Others that have appeared in
English translation are* The Eternal Smile and Other Stories *(1954),*
The Sybil *(1958),* The Death of Ahasuerus *(1962),* Pilgrim at Sea
(1964), and The Holy Land *(1966). They center around man's search
for meaning, the problem of love and destructiveness, the enigma of man's
soul. The author has been living just outside Stockholm since 1930.*

A Note on the Type

The text of this book has been set in Monotype Bulmer. This distinguished type face is a competent recutting of a type, long famous in the history of English printing, that was designed and cut by William Martin about 1790 for William Bulmer of the Shakespeare Press. In design, it is all but a modern face, with vertical stress, sharp differentiation between the thick and thin strokes, and nearly flat serifs. The decorative italic shows the influence of Baskerville, whose pupil Martin was.

The book was composed, printed, and bound by Kingsport Press, Inc., Kingsport, Tennessee. Woodcut decorations by James Grashow. Design by Betty Anderson.